Contents

Revision: recognition of graphemes 1

A **grapheme** is the written representation of a sound.
Point to each grapheme and say its sound.

j	m	n	f	ff	r
s		v		w	sh
ng		th		ph	wh

Point to each grapheme.
Say the different sounds made by this grapheme in each word.

c	cup	ice
g	get	gent
ch	chip	chef
i	pin	kind

o	not	cold
u	cup	music
a	cap	was
e	beg	be

FOCUS ● practise recognition and recall of graphemes
● revise alternative pronunciations of graphemes from Phase Five Book 2

Different spellings of the **w** sound

◗ Look at the **graphemes** that make the **w** sound at the start of these words.

wind

wheel

◗ A **w** sound is missing from each word below.
Is it spelt **w** or **wh**?
Write in the correct spelling.

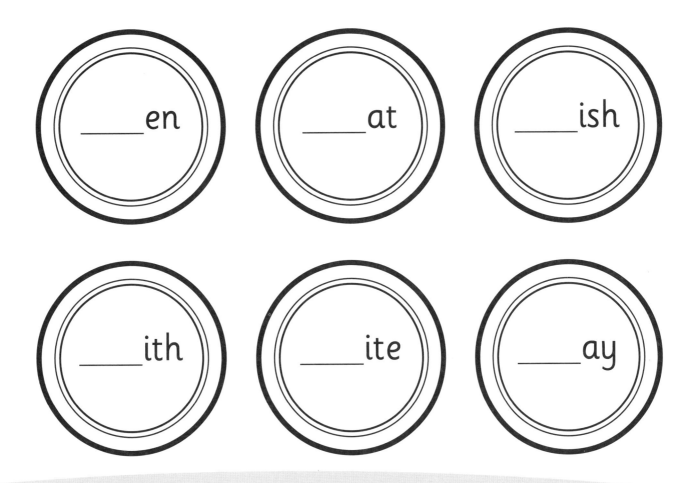

___en

___at

___ish

___ith

___ite

___ay

FOCUS ● revise **w** and **wh** as alternative spellings of the **phoneme w**
● select the correct spelling of the phoneme **w** in **high-frequency words**

5

Different spellings of the **f** sound

Look at the **graphemes** that make the **f** sound in these words.

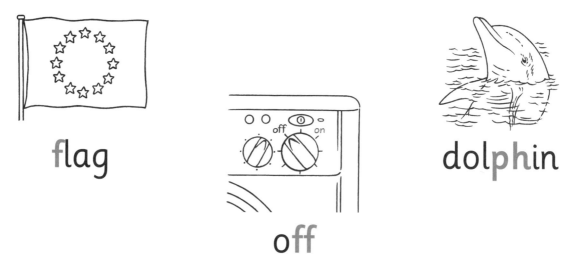

flag

off

dolphin

A **f** sound is missing from each word below.
Is it spelt **f, ff** or **ph**?
Write in the correct spelling.

hu___   ___ell   ___oto

___eet   ___or   ___rom

___un   gra___   ___ood

___irst   ___ish   ___ox

pu___   ___rog   ___one

o___   ___ly   ___ast

FOCUS   ● revise **f, ff** and **ph** as alternative spellings of the **phoneme f**
● select the correct spelling of the phoneme **f** in **high-frequency words**
For **spelling patterns to remember**, see **Notes for parents and other helpers** (page 46).

Different spellings of the **c** sound

Look at the **graphemes** that make the **c** sound in these words.

cat

sack

kangaroo

chemist

A **c** sound is missing from each word below.
Is it spelt **c**, **ck**, **k** or **ch**?
Write in the correct spelling.

so___	li___e	as___	loo___
par___	si___	ba___	du___
too___	ki___	___ome	___at
___old	___ing	___ eep	
___an	___ould	s___ool	

FOCUS   • revise **c**, **ck**, **k** and **ch** as alternative spellings of the **phoneme c**
  • select the correct spelling of the **phoneme c** in **high-frequency words**
For **spelling patterns to remember**, see **Notes for parents and other helpers** (page 46).

7

Different spellings of the **ch** sound

Look at the **graphemes** that make the **ch** sound in these words.

ben**ch**   ma**tch**

Use **sound talk** to read each word below.
Underline the grapheme that makes the **ch** sound.
Colour the match if the word ends with **tch**.

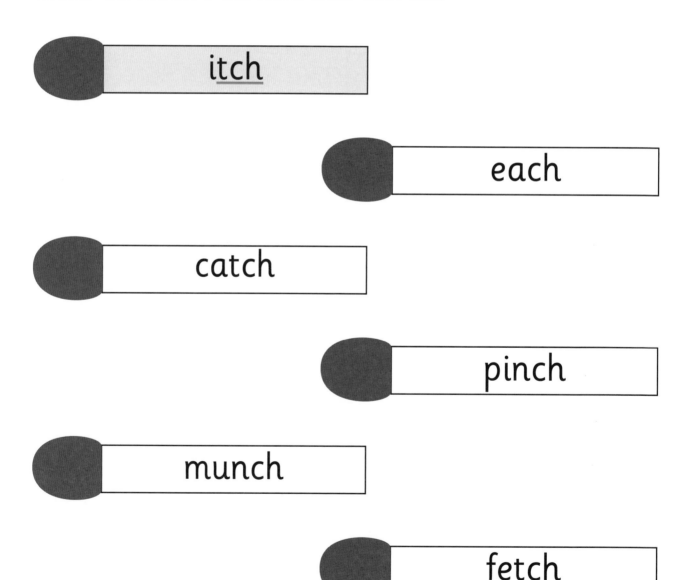

itch

each

catch

pinch

munch

fetch

FOCUS   ● recognise **tch** as an alternative spelling for the **phoneme ch** at the end of words
● develop an awareness of words that use this spelling
● practise reading words by sounding and **blending (blending for reading)**
For **spelling patterns to remember**, see **Notes for parents and other helpers** (page 46).

Different spellings of the **m** sound

At the end of some words the **m** sound is spelt **mb**.

drum

comb

Read each word below.
Underline the **grapheme** that makes the **m** sound.
Colour the comb if the **m** sound is spelt **mb**.

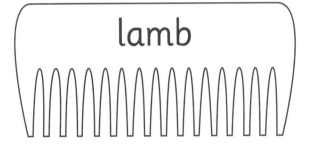

lamb

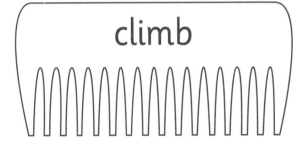

climb

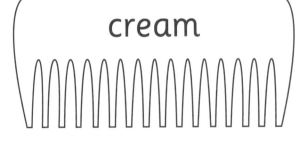

cream

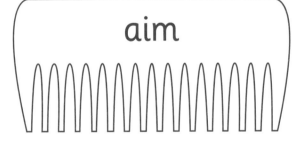

aim

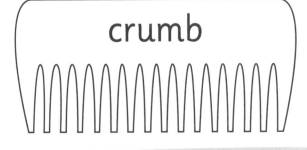

crumb

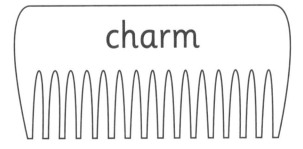

charm

FOCUS • recognise **mb** as an alternative spelling for the **phoneme m** at the end of words
• develop an awareness of words that use this spelling
• practise reading words with adjacent consonants
For **spelling patterns to remember**, see **Notes for parents and other helpers** (page 46).

Different spellings of the **n** sound

Look at the **graphemes** that make the **n** sound at the start of these words.

nest

knit

gnome

Read each word below.
Underline the grapheme that makes the **n** sound.
Write the word in the correct box.

<u>n</u>ear ✔   <u>kn</u>ock ✔   <u>gn</u>aw ✔   gnash

know   nine   knife   gnat

n	kn	gn
near	knock	gnaw

FOCUS ● recognise **kn** and **gn** as alternative spellings for the **phoneme n** at the start of words
● sort words to develop an awareness of which words use which spelling
● practise reading words with vowel graphemes
For **spelling patterns to remember**, see **Notes for parents and other helpers** (page 46).

Different spellings of the r sound

At the start of some words the **r** sound is spelt **wr**.
Look at the **graphemes** that make the **r** sound at the start of these words.

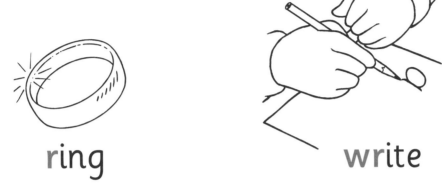

ring   write

Read each word below.
Underline the grapheme that makes the **r** sound.
Write the word in the correct box.

<u>r</u>ipe ✔   <u>wr</u>ap ✔   raw   roast

wrong   real   wrote   wreck

r	wr
ripe	wrap

FOCUS   • recognise **wr** as an alternative spelling for the **phoneme r** at the start of words
        • sort words to develop an awareness of words that use this spelling
        • practise reading words with vowel graphemes and adjacent consonants   11

Spelling choices: **ch**, **m**, **n** and **r**

Write the word to go with each picture.

Say the word in **sound talk** as you write it.

Think carefully about the correct spelling for each sound.

punch

b

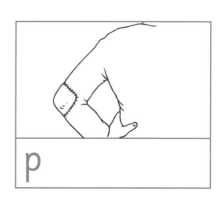

p

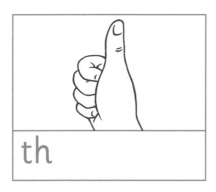

th

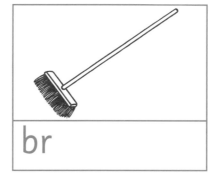

br

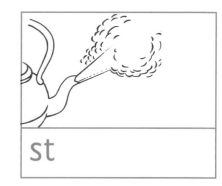

st

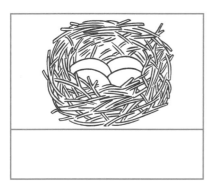

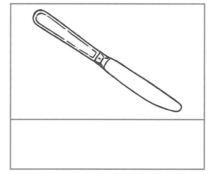

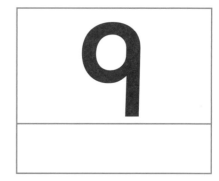

n

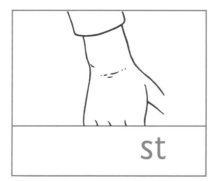

st

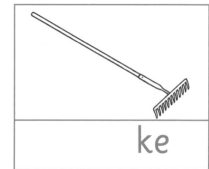

ke

FOCUS • develop an awareness of spelling choices
• **segment** (break up) words, making the correct spelling choice for each **phoneme** (sound)

Writing sentences: **looked**, **called**, **asked**

▶ Read these **tricky words**.
Look out for the tricky parts.
Write over the letters to help you learn to spell the word.

looked   called   asked

▶ Read each sentence.
Write in the missing word.

The teacher _____ cross.

The child _____ for some bread.

There was once a boy _____ Joe.

The man _____ the king for gold.

The thief _____ for jewels to steal.

FOCUS   ● spell the tricky words **looked, called** and **asked**
        ● practise reading and writing sentences, applying phonic knowledge from Phase Five

13

Different spellings of the v sound

▶ A **v** sound at the end of a word is not spelt **v**.
It is spelt **ve**.

van

dove

▶ A **v** sound is missing from each word below.
Is it spelt **v** or **ve**?
Write in the correct spelling.

___ery

li___

___ote

___anish

lea___

sol___

FOCUS ● recognise **ve** as the spelling for the **phoneme v** at the end of words
       ● use this knowledge to make the correct spelling choice

Different spellings of the j sound

▶ A **j** sound at the end of a word is not spelt **j**.
It is often spelt **dge**.

jam

bri**dge**

▶ A **j** sound is missing from each word below.
Is it spelt **j** or **dge**?
Write in the correct spelling.

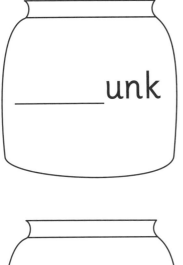

_____unk

_____ab

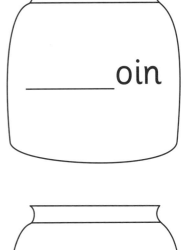

_____oin

fu_____

_____olly

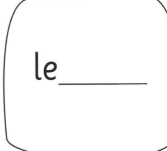

le_____

FOCUS • recognise **dge** as a spelling for the **phoneme j** at the end of words
• use this knowledge to make the correct spelling choice
For **spelling patterns to remember**, see **Notes for parents and other helpers** (page 46).

15

Different spellings of the **s** sound

▶ Look at the **graphemes** that make the **s** sound in these words.

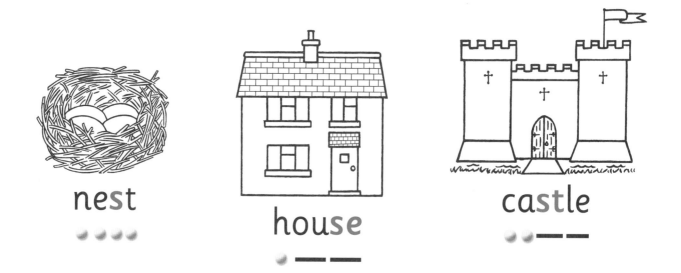

nest

house

castle

▶ Use **sound talk** to read each word below.
Underline the grapheme that makes the **s** sound.
Write the word in the correct box.

<u>s</u>mell ✔   crea<u>se</u> ✔   li<u>st</u>en ✔   nurse

whisper   snow   case   whistle

s	se	st
smell	crease	listen

FOCUS ● recognise **se** and **st** as alternative spellings for the **phoneme s**
● sort words to develop an awareness of which words use which spelling

Revision: spelling choices

Use **sound talk** to read each word below.
The wrong **grapheme** has been used for one sound in each word.
Write the word with the correct grapheme.

foto	photo	lam	
wen		rote	
skool		hav	
mutch		brij	
nock		lisen	

FOCUS   ● recognise incorrect spellings and try alternative graphemes

Different spellings of the **e** sound

▶ Look at the **graphemes** that make the **e** sound in these words.

net

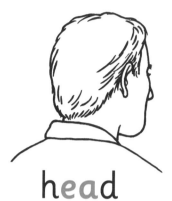

head

▶ Read each line of words.
Look for the word where the **e** sound is spelt **ea**.
Draw a ring round it.

neck	tent	deaf	belt	nest
next	step	speck	bread	slept
sent	crept	ready	spend	chest
melting	seven	feather		tennis
desktop		meadow		helper
chestnut		headstand		bedroom

FOCUS
• recognise **ea** as an alternative spelling for the **phoneme e**
• develop an awareness of words that use this spelling
• practise reading words with one and two **syllables**

Different spellings of the **o** sound

◗ After a **w** sound an **o** sound is sometimes spelt with the letter **a**, like this.

w**a**sp

◗ Use **sound talk** to read the words below.
Draw a ring round the words where an **o** sound is made by the letter **a**.

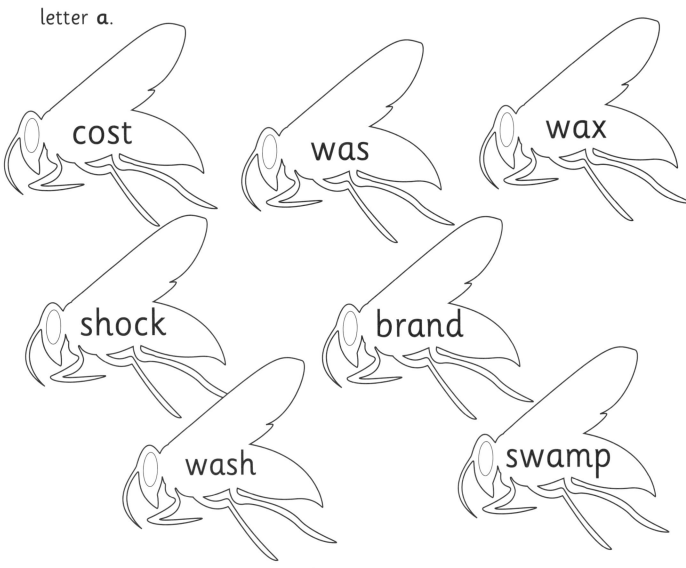

cost

was

wax

shock

brand

wash

swamp

FOCUS ● recognise the 'w special': when the **phoneme o** comes after the phoneme **w** it is spelt **a**
● develop an awareness of words that use this spelling

Revision: recognition of graphemes 2

Point to each **grapheme** and say its sound.

ai	ee	igh	oa	oo	ar
or	ur	oi	ear	air	ay	oy
ir	ue	aw	ew	oe	au	ey
a-e	e-e	i-e	o-e	u-e

Point to each grapheme.
Say the different sounds made by this grapheme in each word.

ow	down	low
ie	pie	chief
ea	sea	head

er	summer		her
ou	out		you
y	yes	my	happy

FOCUS   • practise recognition and recall of graphemes
           • revise alternative pronunciations of graphemes from Phase Five Book 2

Different spellings of the **long a** sound

▶ Look at the **graphemes** that make the **long a** sound in these words.

r**ai**n   tr**ay**   c**a**k**e**

▶ Read each sentence.
Draw a ring round each word with a **long a** sound in it.
Underline the grapheme that makes the **long a** sound.
Write the word in the correct box.

Kay made her way to the bay.

We went sailing but the rain fell again.

Jake and I played a great game.

I was late for the train.

ai	ay	a-e	Other spellings
_____	_____	_____	_____
_____	_____	_____	_____
_____	_____	_____	_____
_____	_____	_____	_____

FOCUS ● practise reading sentences, **blending** words where necessary (**blending for reading**)
        ● identify common ways of spelling the **long a phoneme** in words
        ● sort words to develop knowledge of spelling choices
        For **spelling patterns to remember**, see **Notes for parents and other helpers** (page 46).

Spelling choices: the **long a** sound

All these words have a **long a** sound in them.
Write the word to go with each picture.
Think carefully about the correct spelling for the **long a** sound.
Is it spelt **ai**, **ay** or **a-e**?

rain

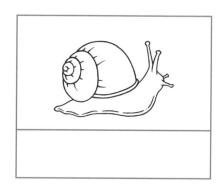

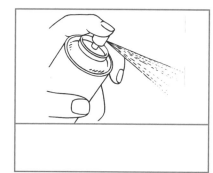

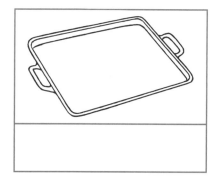

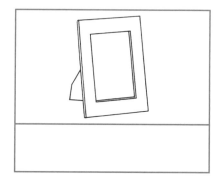

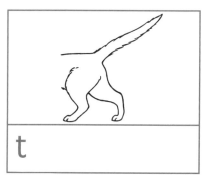

t

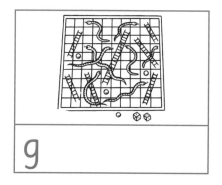

g

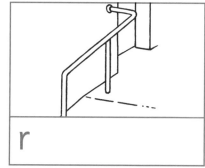

r

FOCUS   ● develop an awareness of spelling choices
          ● make correct spelling choices for the **long a phoneme**

Different spellings of the **long ee** sound

▸ Look at the **graphemes** that make the **long ee** sound in these words.

feet   seat   swede   field

▸ Read each sentence.
Draw a ring round each word with a **long ee** sound in it.
Underline the grapheme that makes the **long ee** sound.
Write the word in the correct box.

He saw the chief thief in the field.

Pete can take these to Steve.

We saw three bees last week.

The stream leads people to the beach.

ee	ea	e-e	ie	Other spellings
_____	_____	_____	_____	_____
_____	_____	_____	_____	_____
_____	_____	_____	_____	_____

FOCUS • practise reading sentences, **blending** words where necessary (**blending for reading**)
• identify common ways of spelling the **long ee phoneme** in words
• sort words to develop knowledge of spelling choices

23

Spelling choices: the **long ee** sound

Use **sound talk** to read each word below.
The wrong **grapheme** has been used for the **long ee** sound in each word.
Write the word with the correct grapheme.

sh**ee**	she	tr**ea**	
sl**ea**p		gr**ea**n	
eet		qu**e**ne	
th**ee**s		sh**ea**p	
b**e**de		f**ee**ld	

FOCUS • recognise incorrect spellings of the **long ee phoneme** and try alternative graphemes

Different spellings of the **long i** sound

▶ Look at the **graphemes** that make the **long i** sound in these words.

l**igh**t   p**ie**   k**i**t**e**   fl**y**

▶ Read each sentence.
Draw a ring round each word with a **long i** sound in it.
Underline the grapheme that makes the **long i** sound.
Write the word in the correct box.

The sun was high in the sky.

Ed let me ride his bike last night.

I tried the pie but fried eggs are nicer.

Why is this bright child so shy?

igh	ie	i-e	y	Other spellings
_____	_____	_____	_____	_____
_____	_____	_____	_____	_____
_____	_____	_____	_____	_____

FOCUS   ● practise reading sentences, **blending** words where necessary (**blending for reading**)
● identify common ways of spelling the **long i phoneme** in words
● sort words to develop knowledge of spelling choices
For **spelling patterns to remember**, see **Notes for parents and other helpers** (page 46).

Spelling choices: the **long i** sound

Write the word to go with each picture.

Think carefully about the correct spelling for the **long i** sound.

Is it spelt **igh**, **ie**, **i-e** or **y**?

night

cr

m

b

FOCUS   ● develop an awareness of spelling choices
          ● make correct spelling choices for the **long i phoneme**

Writing sentences: **Mr** and **Mrs**

▶ Read these **tricky words**.
Write over the letters to help you learn to spell the word.

Mr   Mrs

▶ Read the sentence.
Look at the picture.
Then write another sentence about Mrs Blake.

Mrs Blake is in the garden.

_____

_____

_____

▶ Look at the picture.
Now write a sentence about Mr Green.

_____

_____

Different spellings of the **long o** sound

▶ Look at the **graphemes** that make the **long o** sound in these words.

bo**at   t**o**e   b**o**ne   sn**o**w**

▶ Read each sentence.
Draw a ring round each word with a **long o** sound in it.
Underline the grapheme that makes the **long o** sound.
Write the word in the correct box.

I wrote a note while on the phone.

Joe shows Mo he has grown.

Joan moans about her toe.

The crow goes down the road.

oa	oe	o-e	ow	Other spellings
_____	_____	_____	_____	_____
_____	_____	_____	_____	_____
_____	_____	_____	_____	_____

FOCUS   ● practise reading sentences, **blending** words where necessary (**blending for reading**)
● identify common ways of spelling the **long o phoneme** in words
● sort words to develop knowledge of spelling choices
For **spelling patterns to remember**, see **Notes for parents and other helpers** (page 46).

Spelling choices: the **long o** sound

Write the word to go with each picture.

Think carefully about the correct spelling for the **long o** sound.

Is it spelt **oa**, **oe**, **o-e** or **ow**?

boat

r

h

h

Reading speech bubbles: tricky word **oh**

▶ Read this **tricky word**.
Write over the letters to help you learn to spell the word.

oh   oh

▶ Read each speech bubble.
Write in the missing words.

<u>Oh</u> dear I have lost my <u>case</u>.

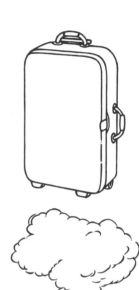

_____ no. I can see _____.

_____ no it is starting to _____.

_____ no the _____ is open.

FOCUS ● spell the tricky word **oh**
● **segment** and spell words, choosing the correct spelling for long vowel sounds (**segmenting for spelling**)

Different spellings of the **long oo** sound

Look at the **graphemes** that make the **long oo** sound in these words.

moon   blue   June   screw

Read each line of words.
Underline the grapheme that makes the **long oo** sound in each word.
Draw a ring round the word with the different spelling.

moon	soon	spoon	prune	noon
root	toot	flute	shoot	boot
cool	school	tool	rule	stool
grew	threw	true	screw	drew
broom	plume	bloom	gloom	zoom
zoo	stew	knew	pew	new

Spelling two-part words: the **long oo** sound

Say the word to go with the picture.

Listen for the two parts.

Write the **graphemes** to make the missing part of the word.

_____bell

bed_____

sham_____

_____ing gum

ig_____

_____paste

FOCUS   ● spell words with two parts
                        ● make correct spelling choices for the **long oo phoneme**

Revision: alternative graphemes 1

Write the other spellings for each of these sounds.

long a sound   <u>ai</u>

long ee sound   <u>ee</u>

long i sound   <u>igh</u>

long o sound   <u>oa</u>

long oo sound   <u>oo</u>

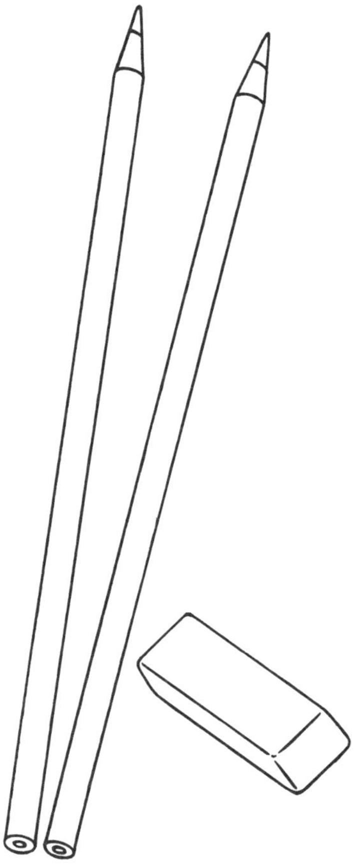

FOCUS   ● write the common **graphemes** for long vowel sounds

Reading and spelling two-part words

Look at the **graphemes** that make the **long ee** sound at the end of these words.

happ**y**

chimn**ey**

Read each word below.
Underline the grapheme that makes the **long ee** sound at the end of the word.
Write the word in the correct box.

sunn**y** ✔   donk**ey** ✔   trolley   money

lady   very   rainy   turkey

y	ey
sunny	donkey

FOCUS ● revise **y** and **ey** as alternative spellings for the **long ee phoneme** at the end of words
● sort words to develop an awareness of words that use these spellings
● read words with two parts

Writing sentences: **their** and **people**

▶ Read these **tricky words**.
Look out for the tricky parts.
Write over the letters to help you learn to spell the word.

their their   **people** people

▶ Read each sentence.
Write in the missing words.

Some <u>people</u> like butter on <u>their</u> toast.

Some _____ grow herbs
in _____ garden.

Some _____ have milk in _____ tea.

Some _____ watch _____ team play.

Some _____ eat _____ food fast.

FOCUS   • spell the tricky words **their** and **people**
• practise reading and writing sentences, sounding and **blending** words where necessary (**blending for reading**)
• check that sentences make sense   35

Different spellings of the **or** sound

Look at the **graphemes** that make the **or** sound in these words.

horn

4
four

ball

Read each word below.
Underline the grapheme that makes the **or** sound.
Write the word in the correct box.

sp<u>or</u>t ✔   p<u>our</u> ✔   t<u>al</u>k ✔   walk

morning   call   your   sort

or	our	al
sport	pour	talk

FOCUS ● recognise **our** and **al** as alternative ways of spelling the **phoneme or**
● sort words to develop an awareness of which words use which spelling

Different spellings of the **ur** sound

▶ Look at the **graphemes** that make the **ur** sound in these words.

church   girl   fern   earth

▶ Use **sound talk** to read each word below.
Underline the grapheme that makes the **ur** sound.
Write the word in the correct box.

h<u>ur</u>t ✔   b<u>ir</u>th ✔   t<u>er</u>m ✔   h<u>ea</u>rd ✔

third   burn   turn   sir

learn   earn   her   kerb

ur	ir	er	ear
hurt	birth	term	heard

FOCUS   ● revise **ur**, **ir** and **er** as alternative spellings for the **phoneme ur**
        ● recognise the alternative pronunciation of **ear**
        ● sort words to develop an awareness of which words use which spelling   37

Different spellings of the **ow** sound

Look at the **graphemes** that make the **ow** sound in these words.

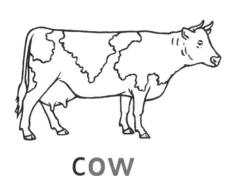

cow

cloud

An **ow** sound is missing from each word below.
Is it spelt **ow** or **ou**?
Write in the correct spelling.

ab____t

br____n

s____nd

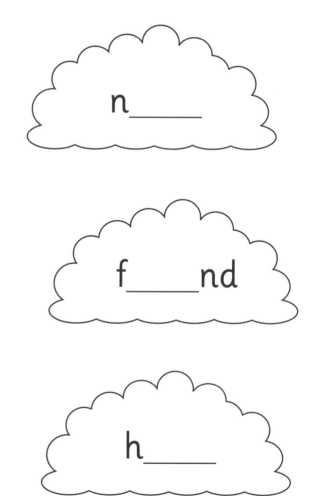

n____

f____nd

h____

FOCUS • revise **ow** and **ou** as alternative spellings of the **phoneme ow**
• select the correct spelling of the phoneme **ow** in **high-frequency words**
For **spelling patterns to remember**, see **Notes for parents and other helpers** (page 46).

Different spellings of the **oi** sound

▶ An **oi** sound at the end of a word is not spelt **oi**.
It is spelt **oy**.

coin

boy

▶ An **oi** sound is missing from each word below.
Is it spelt **oi** or **oy**?
Write in the correct spelling.

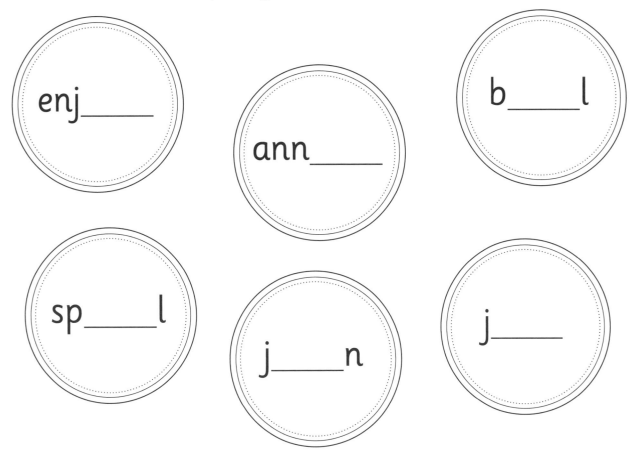

enj____

ann____

b____l

sp____l

j____n

j____

FOCUS ● revise **oi** and **oy** as alternative spellings of the **phoneme oi**
● select the correct spelling of the phoneme **oi**
For **spelling patterns to remember**, see **Notes for parents and other helpers** (page 46).

39

Different spellings of the **ear** sound

▶ Look at the **graphemes** that make the **ear** sound in these words.

ear

ch**eer**

▶ Use **sound talk** to read each of the rhyming words below.
Underline the grapheme that makes the **ear** sound.
Write the word in the correct box.

n<u>ear</u> ✔   p<u>eer</u> ✔   h<u>ere</u> ✔   hear

sneer   jeer   smear   clear

ear	**eer**	Other spellings
near	peer	here
_____	_____	_____
_____	_____	_____
_____	_____	_____

FOCUS ● recognise **eer** as an alternative spelling of the **phoneme ear**
● sort words to develop an awareness of which word uses which spelling

Different spellings of the **air** sound

Look at the **graphemes** that make the **air** sound in these words.

ch**air**   b**ear**   squ**are**

Use **sound talk** to read each of the rhyming words below.
Underline the grapheme that makes the **air** sound.
Write the word in the correct box.

p<u>ai</u>r ✔   w<u>ea</u>r ✔   c<u>are</u> ✔   share

fair   dare   pear   stair

air	**ear**	**are**
pair	wear	care

Revision: alternative graphemes 2

Write another spelling for each of these sounds.

or _____

ur _____

ow _____

oi _____

ear _____

air _____

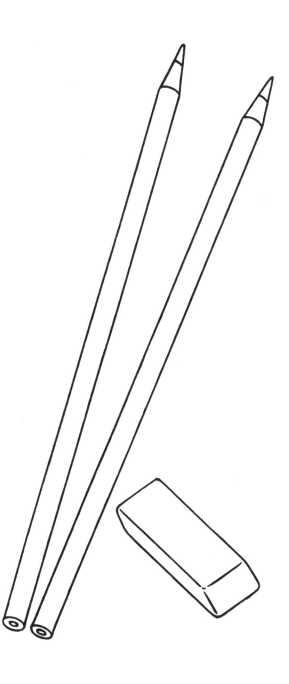

FOCUS ● write the common **graphemes** for long vowel sounds

Assessment 1: sound check

1 Point to each **grapheme** below and ask the child to say its sound.

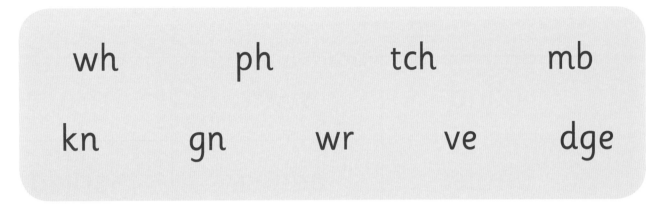

wh	ph	tch	mb
kn	gn	wr	ve	dge

2 Point to each grapheme below and ask the child to say its sound or sounds. Please note that further lists of graphemes are given on pages 4, 20, 33 and 42 (opposite).

ar	er	ay	ou	ie	ea
oy	ir	ue	aw	ew	oe
au	ey	a-e	e-e	i-e	o-e
u-e		eer		are	our

3 Say a sound made by any of the above and ask the child to point to possible graphemes.

Assessment 2:
blending and segmenting check

1 Check the child's **blending for reading**. Ask the child both to say the sounds and then **blend** them to make each word. Note whether the child tries alternative pronunciations of **graphemes**.

blind	swift	grace
ginger	bellow	spied
shriek	ready	steamer
mermaid	spying	squash

2 Check the child's **segmenting for spelling** by asking him or her to spell the word to go with each picture below. Ask the child to say the word in **sound talk** and then write the letters needed.

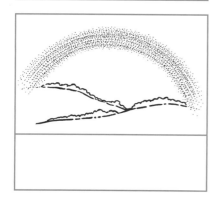

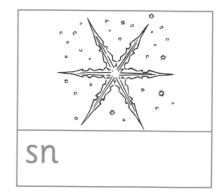

sn

Assessment 3: high-frequency word check

Ask the child to read these **high-frequency words**. **Please note:** this is just a very small sample of the 100 high-frequency words that the children should now recognise automatically and begin to spell correctly.

looked	called	asked	their
people	oh	Mr	Mrs

Assessment statements

Run through with the child these assessment statements. Begin, 'Here is a list of the things you can do.'

I can give the sound when shown any of the **graphemes** on page 43.	
I can write possible graphemes for any given sound.	
I can **blend** and read one- and two-part words like those on page 44.	
I can **segment** and spell one- and two-part words like those on page 44.	
I can read automatically high-frequency words like those above.	
I can spell high-frequency words like those above.	
I can write each letter correctly when doing the activities.	

What next?

You are now ready for **Sound Phonics Phase Six Book 1**.

At this stage, children will often spell words in a phonically plausible way but may not use the conventional spelling. Parents and other helpers, please see page 46 overleaf for further notes on this point.

Notes for parents and other helpers

Spelling at the end of Phase Five

At this stage, children often spell words in a way that is phonically plausible but incorrect (for example, they may spell **make** as **maik**) – and this is normal in this phase of development. Learning to spell each word correctly is a long process, which begins in Phase Five and continues in Phase Six and beyond. When the child makes the wrong choice of **graphemes**, tell him or her the correct spelling and note next time whether or not it has been remembered. You can also point out patterns and rules, such as those listed below, which will make it easier for the child to choose the correct spelling.

Spelling patterns to remember

page 6	**f, ff, ph**	• **f** is the usual grapheme for this sound • **ff** comes at the end of short words following short vowel sounds (**cliff, puff**) • **ph** is used in a few words only (**phone, photo**): encourage the child to learn them
page 7	**c, ck, k, ch**	• **ck** is used after a short vowel • **k** is used after a consonant or long vowel • very few words use **ch** (**chemist, school**) and very few end with **c** (**picnic**): encourage the child to learn them
page 8	**ch, tch** at the end of a word	• **tch** is most likely at the end of a word with a short vowel sound • there are common exceptions to this rule (**much, such, rich**) • **ch** usually follows a long vowel sound or a consonant (**march, torch**)
page 9	**m, mb** at the end of a word	• **mb** is only used at the end of a few words (**comb, limb**): encourage the child to learn them
page 10	**n, kn, gn** at the start of a word	• **kn** and **gn** are only used at the start of a few words (**know, gnaw**): encourage the child to learn them
page 15	**j, dge** at the end of a word	• **ge** is an alternative ending used in some words (**page, huge**)
page 21	**ai, ay, a-e**	• **ay** is the usual spelling for a **long a** sound at the end of a word • **ai** is often followed by **n** or **l** • **a-e** is usually the correct spelling with other letters (–**ake**, –**ape**, –**ate**) • there are some rarer spellings: **eigh** (**eight**), **ey** (**they**) and **ea** (**great**)
page 25	**igh, ie, i-e, y**	• **igh** is often followed by **t**, to make **ight** • **i-e** is the correct spelling with most other letters (–**ile**, –**ime**, –**ike**) • at the end of a word the **long i** sound is likely to be **y** (**sky, fly**)
page 28	**oa, oe, o-e, ow**	• **ow** and **oe** are the most common spellings for a **long o** sound at the end of a word • **oa** and **o-e** are most often found in the middle of a word
page 38	**ow, ou**	• **ou** is never found making this sound at the end of words
page 39	**oi, oy**	• **oi** is the usual spelling for the **oi** sound in the middle of a word • **oy** is the usual spelling for this sound at the end of a word